S0-BKG-792

FROM THE FIELD

Mark Zelinski

Published by:
From the Heart Publishing
119 Duncairn Crescent
Hamilton, Ontario, Canada L9C 6E9
Telephone: 905 630-2556
E mail: fromtheheart@interlog.com
Web: www.fromtheheart.ca

Photographs copyright © 2010 by Mark Zelinski Photographic Design
Painting copyright © 1976 by Mark Zelinski
Text copyright © 2008 by From the Heart Publishing

All rights reserved. No part of this book may be reproduced or transmitted in any form or by any means, electronic or mechanical, including photocopying, scanning, recording, or by any information storage and retrieval system, without the written permission of the publisher.

Scans and colour proofs by Bochsler Creative Solutions, Burlington, Ontario www.bcreativesolutions.com
Printed in Hong Kong by Paramount Printing Co. Ltd.

ISBN 978-0-9685879-5-9

Cover and book design by Mark Zelinski and Louise Marie Vien

For information about the work of Mark Zelinski, purchasing books, limited edition prints or photographs visit www.MarkZelinski.com

Printed on recycled paper

INTO THE FIELD

Before the beginning, even before the ocean came into being, a seed drifted through emptiness and into the dimension of time. Time allowed a dimension of new physical possibility. Eventually the seed landed onto a circular rock and was stuck to it. Elements combined, and in concert created an atmosphere in which the seed was transformed. A root stretched into the soil, strengthened its grip and reached for water to satisfy its new thirst. A tiny shoot sprung into the air, nourished by a distant fire.

The shoot grew into a tree, large and upright. Many creatures began to rest on its limbs. Some took pieces from it to make nests and tools. Some burned its bark for warmth. Others scratched their name into it. Seasons passed.

One day, a smaller rock flew close by. The tree felt the tug. It was time to leave the rock which had become its home. The tree had grown larger than the rock and if it did not leave, the rock would die.

The tree knew that it must go but was sad from this. With its left hand the tree encircled the rock gently, drawing its story into the roots. The story passed through wood into its right arm, which the tree held toward the field of its origin. A new branch grew from its right hand and spread into leaves. With his left hand the tree drew knowledge from the kind rock. With the new branch he painted of these wonders into the sky – so that he would never forget the experience of living on that rock.

2

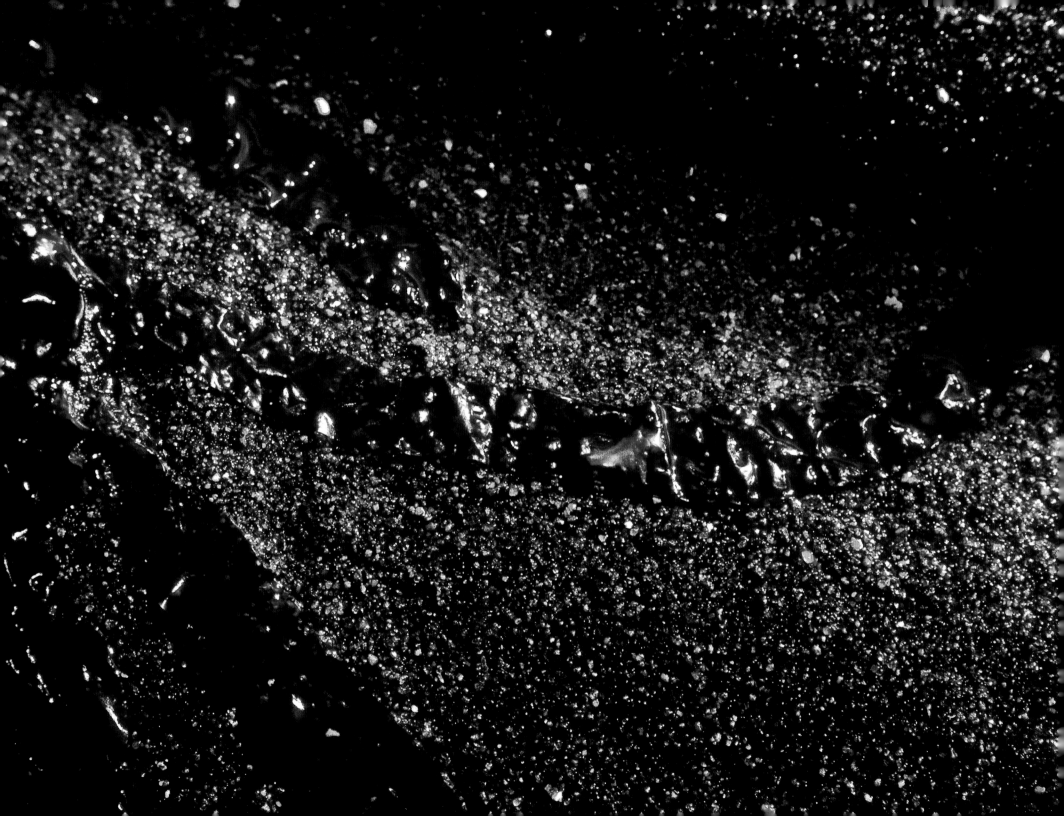

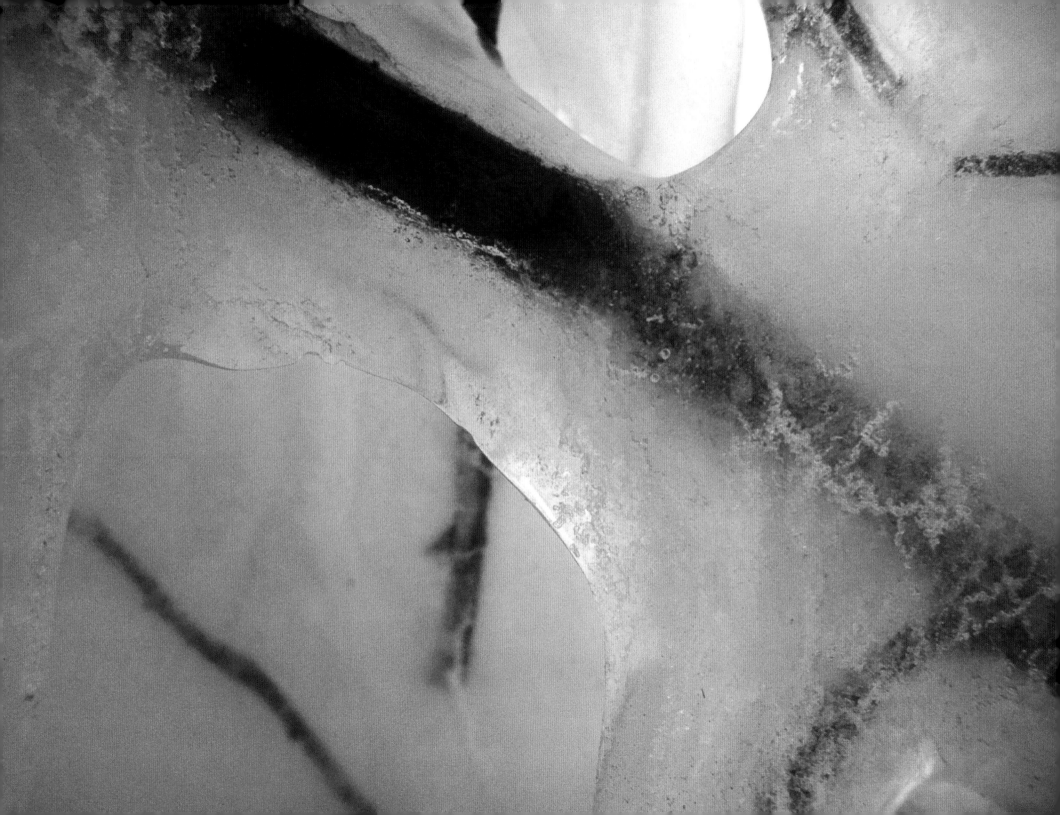

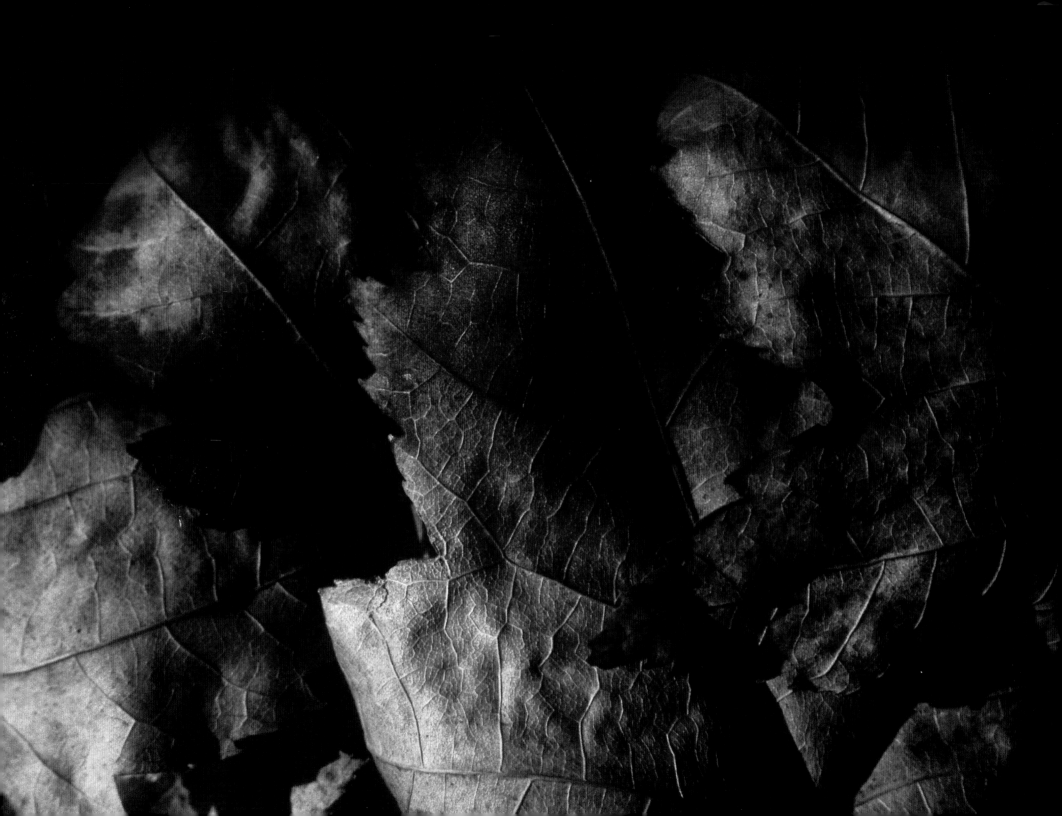

43

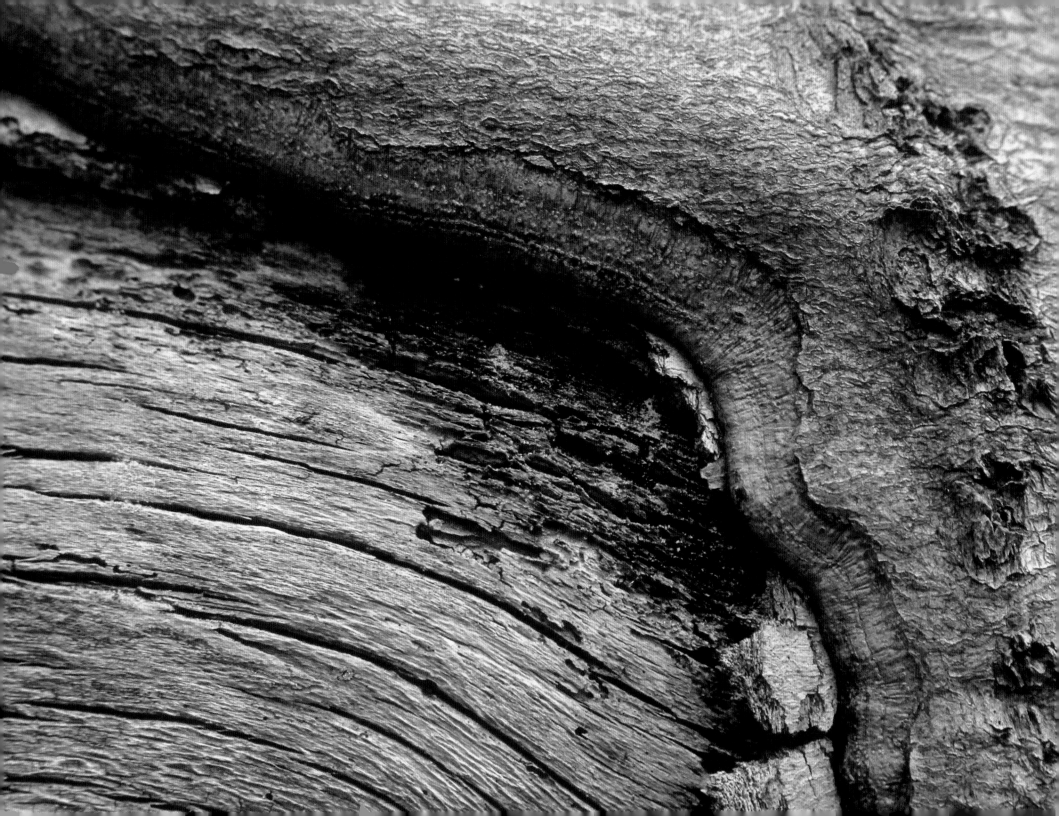

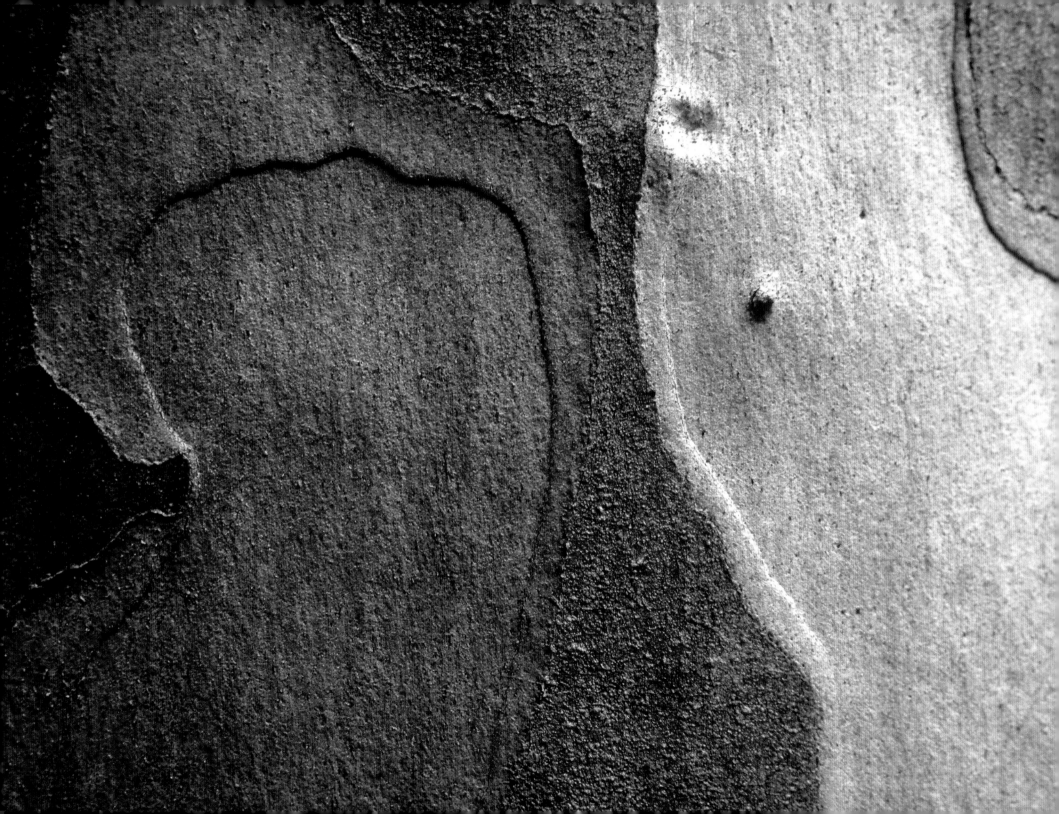

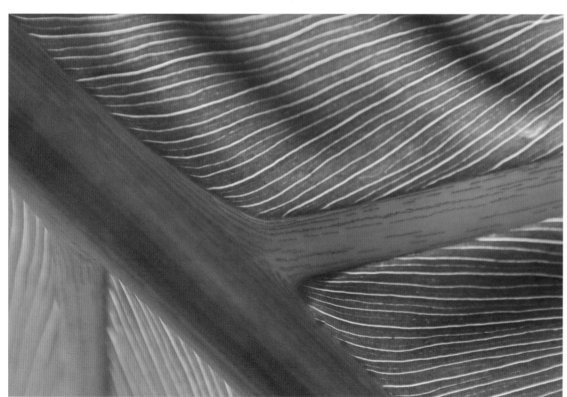

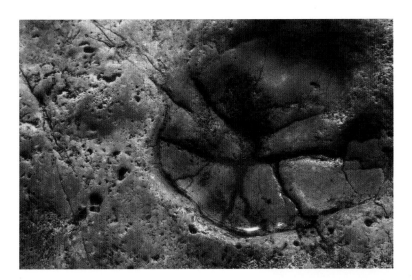

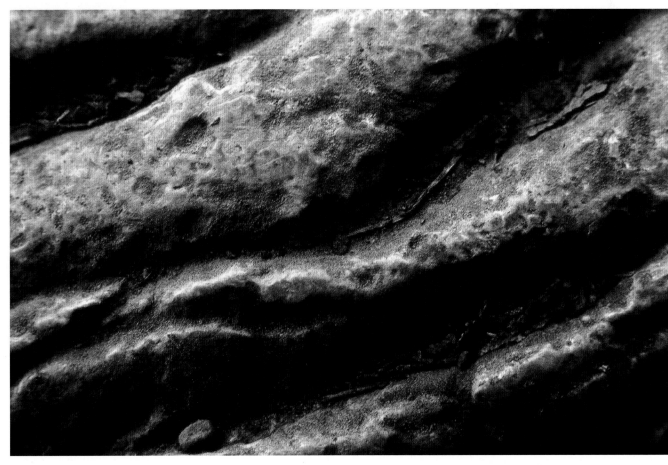

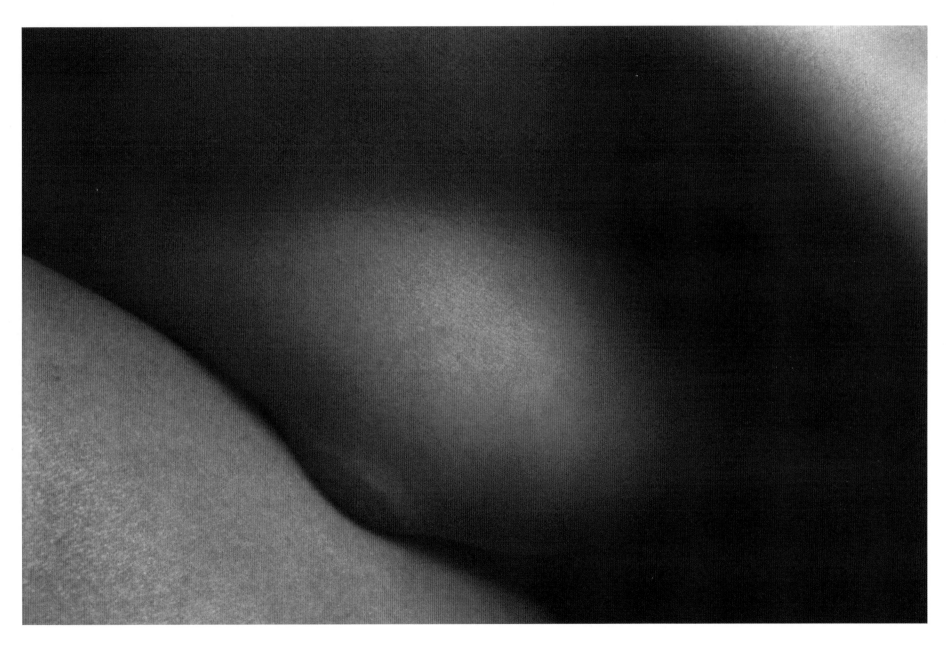

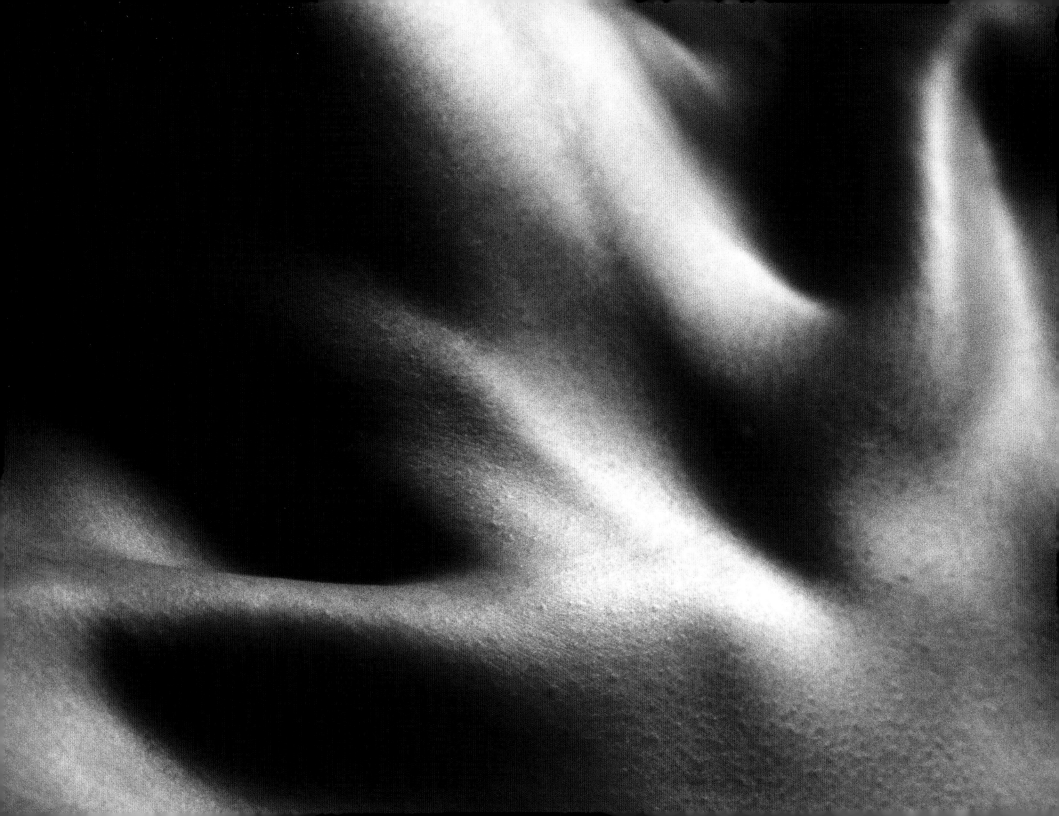

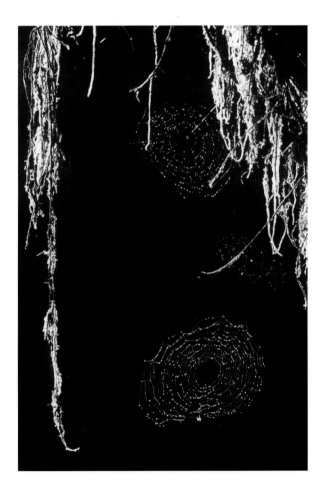

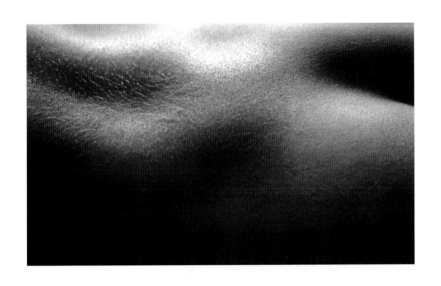

104

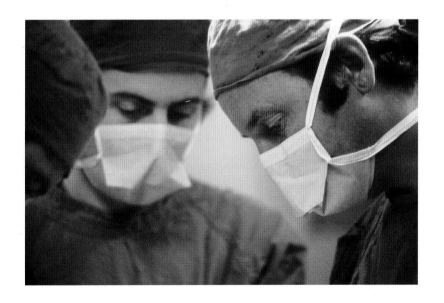

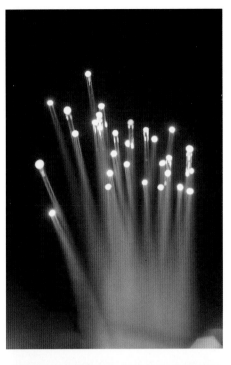

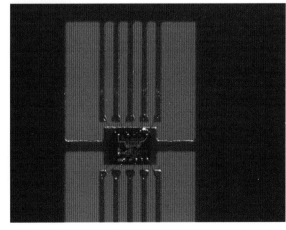

ON THE FIELD

On the field it was hot and dusty. The jackals were hungry and tired of eating dry seeds. After all, they were meant to be carnivores. The sound of laughing annoyed them even more. Nearby, a giraffe munched on the high leaves that none other could reach. The giraffe was entertained by the chattering monkeys who frolicked between the branches and groomed one another.

A watching lizard had a wicked idea. He whispered to the jackals, "I will give you a weapon." The jackals were thrilled. They fed the weapon to the innocent monkeys and they perished. One by one they fell to the ground, but since the weapon was poison the jackals could not claim their prey. The jackals came to the animals of the plain and said, "The monkeys are dying. We must all help them." So the jackals collected gifts and hid them under rocks, and gave only a little to the suffering monkeys.

The giraffe longed to watch them play again.

One morning a white tiger arrived from the domed mountain and said, "I am here to collect on a bill. Who holds the bill?" He looked at the giraffe, who shook her head. He looked at the jackals, who were liars and also shook their heads. He then looked at the lizard who tried to shake his head but couldn't. The lizard nodded instead.

The tiger looked at the lizard quietly. "The debt that you owe is great. How will you pay it?" The lizard looked at the jackals, who feigned innocence. The lizard looked at the tiger and said, "Who are you? There are no tigers here." "I have always been here," the tiger replied.

The lizard nodded his head.

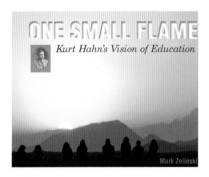

ONE SMALL FLAME: Kurt Hahn's Vision of Education
Mark Zelinski
pub. 2010, From The Heart Publishing
forewords by His Majesty King Constantint and Justin Trudeau
Hardcover, 160 pages, over 240 colour photographs

To commemorate the 90th anniversary of Kurt Hahn's first school, Schule Schloss Salem, award-winning photographer Mark Zelinski traveled to more than 70 Round Square Schools, Outward Bound Centres, and United World Colleges worldwide to capture the human spirit at its most courageous and vulnerable moments. Hahn's visionary ideas are alive in the world today and in constant evolution through the action-based programmes that are so beautifully portrayed in this book.

PLAYING WITH THE ANGELS: Stories of Possibilities For Grieving Children
K. Jane George
Paintings by Mattie Zelinski
pub. 2010, From The Heart Publishing
Hardcover, 40 pages, 12 colour illustrations

"Playing With The Angels" shares a gentle series of short stories about children who have lost a loved one, explores their emotions and responses to their loss, and explains how each child comes to an acceptance (on their own terms.) Each story in this book is based on a real child and their real loss, helping children who are living with grief to realize that they are not alone and to understand their feelings. Realistic storytelling is complemented by a magnificent series of images from artist Mattie Zelinski, capturing the magic, mystery and possibility of what may lie beyond life on this earth.

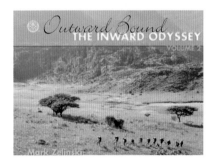

OUTWARD BOUND: THE INWARD ODYSSEY Volume 2
Mark Zelinski
pub. 2002, From The Heart Publishing
foreword by HRH Prince Andrew
Hardcover, 200 pages, over 180 colour photographs

Mark Zelinski takes you on a visual odyssey to remote and breathtaking locations from around the globe. In the words of His Royal Highness Prince Andrew, this book "will serve to inspire future generations of leaders across the world." Through Outward Bound, founder Kurt Hahn's ideas have changed the lives of more than two and a half million participants from all walks of life. "The Inward Odyssey Volume 2" documents the scope, depth and beauty of the Outward Bound experience at 43 schools across 29 countries.

UNITITLED
Hardcover, 120 pages, 150 colour photographs, no text

Diverse, intimate cultural portraits from 70 countries comprise a global family album. A mirror of the human spirit from 1975 – 2009. Not for sale. Available to schools and NGOs through application to fromtheheart@interlog.com

www.fromtheheart.ca